THE BEST GUIT
SONGBOOK EVER

C000263232

Wise Publications
London/New York/Paris/Sydney/Copenhagen/Madrid

Exclusive Distributors:
Music Sales Limited
8/9 Frith Street,
London W1V 5TZ, England.
Music Sales Pty Limited
120 Rothschild Avenue
Rosebery, NSW 2018,
Australia.

Order No. AM954118
ISBN 0-7119-7217-6
This book © Copyright 1998 by Wise Publications
Visit the Internet Music Shop at
http://www.musicsales.co.uk

Book design by Chloë Alexander
Photographs courtesy of London Features International

Printed in the United Kingdom by
Caligraving Limited, Thetford, Norfolk.

Your Guarantee of Quality
As publishers, we strive to produce every book to the highest commercial
standards. The book has been carefully designed to minimise awkward
page turns and to make playing from it a real pleasure. Particular care has been
given to specifying acid-free, neutral-sized paper made from pulps which have not
been elemental chlorine bleached. This pulp is from farmed sustainable forests
and was produced with special regard for the environment. Throughout, the
printing and binding have been planned to ensure a sturdy, attractive publication
which should give years of enjoyment. If your copy fails to meet our high
standards, please inform us and we will gladly replace it.

Music Sales' complete catalogue describes thousands of titles and is available in
full colour sections by subject, direct from Music Sales Limited. Please state your
areas of interest and send a cheque/postal order for £1.50 for postage to:
Music Sales Limited, Newmarket Road, Bury St. Edmunds, Suffolk IP33 3YB.

CONTENTS

ALANIS MORISSETTE

WET WET WET

THE CRANBERRIES

THE LEVELLERS

THE STONE ROSES

PAUL WELLER

PULP

Relative Tuning

The guitar can be tuned with the aid of pitch pipes or dedicated electronic guitar tuners which are available through your local music dealer. If you do not have a tuning device, you can use relative tuning. Estimate the pitch of the 6th string as near as possible to E or at least a comfortable pitch (not too high, as you might break other strings in tuning up). Then, while checking the various positions on the diagram, place a finger from your left hand on the:

5th fret of the E or 6th string and **tune the open A**(or 5th string) to the note (A)

5th fret of the A or 5th string and **tune the open D** (or 4th string) to the note (D)

5th fret of the D or 4th string and **tune the open G** (or 3rd string) to the note (G)

4th fret of the G or 3rd string and **tune the open B** (or 2nd string) to the note (B)

5th fret of the B or 2nd string and **tune the open E** (or 1st string) to the note (E)

E   A   D   G   B   E
or   or   or   or   or   or
6th   5th   4th   3rd   2nd   1st

He

Nu

1st
Fret

2nd
Fret

3rd
Fret

4th
Fret

5th
Fret

Reading Chord Boxes

Chord boxes are diagrams of the guitar neck viewed head upwards, face on as illustrate The top horizontal line is the nut, unless a higher fret number is indicated, the others ar the frets.

The vertical lines are the strings, starting from E (or 6th) on the left to E (or 1st) on the right.

The black dots indicate where to place your fingers.

Strings marked with an O are played open, not fretted.

Strings marked with an X should not be played.

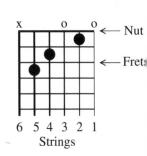

6 5 4 3 2 1
Strings

ALL I REALLY WANT

Music by Alanis Morissette and Glenn Ballard • Lyrics by Alanis Morissette

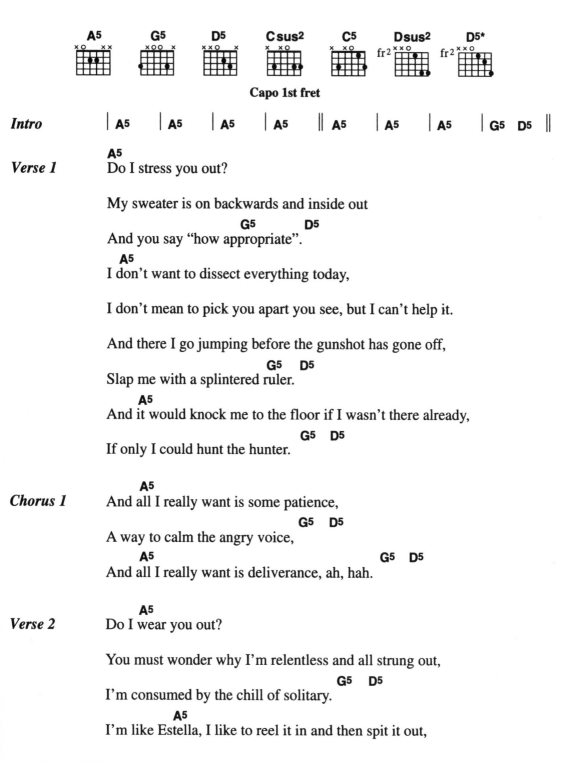

Capo 1st fret

Intro | A5 | A5 | A5 | A5 ‖ A5 | A5 | A5 | G5 D5 ‖

Verse 1

A5
Do I stress you out?

My sweater is on backwards and inside out
 G5   **D5**
And you say "how appropriate".
 A5
I don't want to dissect everything today,

I don't mean to pick you apart you see, but I can't help it.

And there I go jumping before the gunshot has gone off,
 G5   **D5**
Slap me with a splintered ruler.
 A5
And it would knock me to the floor if I wasn't there already,
 G5   **D5**
If only I could hunt the hunter.

Chorus 1

 A5
And all I really want is some patience,
 G5   **D5**
A way to calm the angry voice,
 A5   **G5**   **D5**
And all I really want is deliverance, ah, hah.

Verse 2

 A5
Do I wear you out?

You must wonder why I'm relentless and all strung out,
 G5   **D5**
I'm consumed by the chill of solitary.
 A5
I'm like Estella, I like to reel it in and then spit it out,

G⁵ D⁵
I'm frustrated by your apathy.

A⁵
And I am frightened by the corrupted ways of this land,

G⁵ D⁵
If only I could meet the maker.

A⁵
And I am fascinated by the spiritual man,

G⁵ D⁵
I am humbled by his humble nature,   yeah.

Chorus 2

A⁵
And what I wouldn't give to find a soulmate,

G⁵ D⁵
Someone else to catch this drift,

A⁵   **G⁵ D⁵**
And what I wouldn't give to meet a kindred, ah, hah.

Interlude | **A⁵** | **A⁵** | **A⁵** | **G⁵ D⁵** ‖

Middle

Csus²   **C⁵**   **Dsus²**   **D⁵***
Enough about me, let's talk about you for a minute.

Csus²   **C⁵**   **Dsus²**   **D⁵***
Enough about you, let's talk about life for a while.

Csus²   **C⁵**   **Dsus²**   **D⁵***
The conflicts, the craziness and the sound of pretences falling

A⁵
All around, all around.

Verse 3

(A⁵)
Why are you so petrified of silence?

N.C.
Here, can you handle this?

A⁵
Did you think about bills, your ex, your deadlines,

Or when you think you're gonna die?

Or did you long for the next distraction?

And all I need now is intellectual intercourse,

G⁵   D⁵
A soul to dig the hole much deeper.

A⁵
And I have no concept of time other than it is flying,

G⁵ D⁵
If only I could kill the killer.

Chorus 3　　　‖: And all I really want is some peace, man,

A5

G5 D5

A place to find a common ground,

A5　　　　　　　　　　　　　　**G5 D5**

And all I really want is a wavelength, ah, hah.

A5

And all I really want is some comfort,

G5 D5

A way to get my hands untied,

A5　　　　　　　　　　　**G5 D5**

And all I really want is some justice, ah, hah.　　:‖

Repeat to fade
with ad lib. vocals

HAND IN MY POCKET

Music by Alanis Morissette and Glenn Ballard ▪ Lyrics by Alanis Morissette

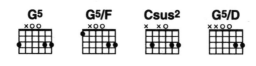

Intro　　| G5　| G5　| G5　| G5　||

Verse 1

G5
I'm broke but I'm happy, I'm poor but I'm kind,

I'm short but I'm healthy, yeah.

I'm high but I'm grounded, I'm sane but I'm overwhelmed,

I'm lost but I'm hopeful baby.

Chorus 1

　　　　　　　　　　　　G5/F　　Csus2
And what it all comes down to
　　　　　　　　　　　　　　G5
Is that everything's gonna be fine, fine, fine,
　　　　　G5/F
'Cause I got one hand in my pocket
　　　Csus2　　　　　　　G5/D　　G5
And the other one is giving a high five.

Verse 2

G5
I feel drunk but I'm sober, I'm young and I'm underpaid,

I'm tired but I'm working, yeah.

I care but I'm restless, I'm here but I'm really gone,

I'm wrong and I'm sorry baby.

Chorus 2

                                      G5/F   **Csus2**
And what it all comes down to

                                        G5
Is that everything's gonna be quite alright,

                 G5/F
'Cos I've got one hand in my pocket

                 Csus2   **G5/D**   **G5**
And the other one is flicking a cigarette.

Solo | **G5** | **G5** | **G5** | **G5** | **G5** | **G5** | **G5** | **G5** ||

Chorus 3

                                        G5/F   **Csus2**
And what it all comes down to

                                          G5
Is that I haven't got it all figured out just yet,

                 G5/F
'Cos I've got one hand in my pocket

                 Csus2   **G5/D**   **G5**
And the other one is giving a peace sign.

Verse 3

                 G5
I'm free but I'm focused, I'm green but I'm wise,

I'm hard but I'm friendly baby.

I'm sad but I'm laughing, I'm brave but I'm chicken shit,

I'm sick but I'm pretty baby.

Chorus 4

                                      G5/F   **Csus2**
And what it all boils down to

                                      G5
Is that no one's got it figured out just yet.

                 G5/F
But I've got one hand in my pocket

                 Csus2   **G5/D**   **G5**
And the other one is playing a piano.

                                        G5/F   **Csus2**
And what it all comes down to my friends

                                      G5
Is that every thing is just fine, fine, fine,

                 G5/F
'Cos I've got one hand in my pocket

                 Csus2   **G5/D**   **G5**
And the other one is hailing a taxi cab.

IRONIC

Music by Alanis Morissette and Glenn Ballard ▪ Lyrics by Alanis Morissette

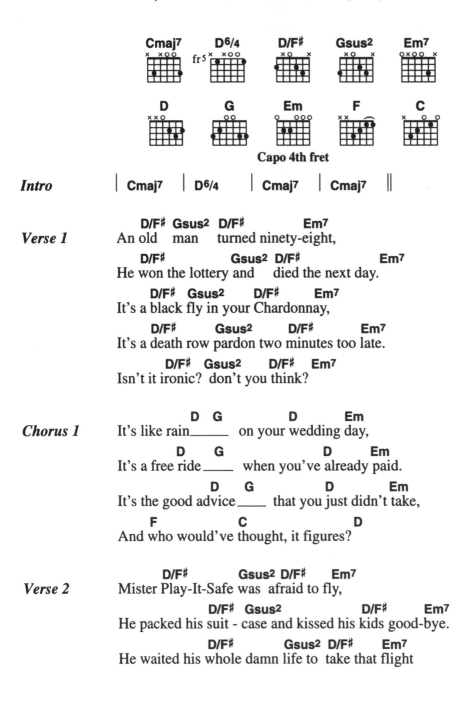

Capo 4th fret

Intro | Cmaj7 | D6/4 | Cmaj7 | Cmaj7 ‖

Verse 1

    D/F♯ Gsus2 D/F♯   Em7
An old man   turned ninety-eight,

    D/F♯   Gsus2 D/F♯   Em7
He won the lottery and   died the next day.

    D/F♯ Gsus2   D/F♯   Em7
It's a black fly in your Chardonnay,

    D/F♯   Gsus2   D/F♯   Em7
It's a death row pardon two minutes too late.

    D/F♯ Gsus2   D/F♯ Em7
Isn't it ironic? don't you think?

Chorus 1

            D G   D   Em
It's like rain_____ on your wedding day,

         D G   D   Em
It's a free ride_____ when you've already paid.

           D G   D   Em
It's the good advice_____ that you just didn't take,

      F   C   D
And who would've thought, it figures?

Verse 2

    D/F♯   Gsus2 D/F♯   Em7
Mister Play-It-Safe was afraid to fly,

        D/F♯ Gsus2   D/F♯   Em7
He packed his suit - case and kissed his kids good-bye.

        D/F♯   Gsus2 D/F♯   Em7
He waited his whole damn life to take that flight

           D/F#   **Gsus2**
And as the plane crashed down he thought,
        D/F#   **Em7**
"Well isn't this nice?"
          D/F# **Gsus2**   **D/F#** **Em7**
And isn't it ironic? don't you think?

Chorus 2   As Chorus 1

          Cmaj7
Bridge   Well life has a funny way of sneaking up
      D6/4
On you when you think everything's okay and
      Cmaj7   **D6/4**
Everything's going right.
          Cmaj7
And life has a funny way of helping you
      D6/4
Out when you think everything's going wrong and
      Cmaj7
Everything blows up in your face.

          D/F# **Gsus2**   **D/F#**   **Em7**
Verse 3   A traffic jam when you're already late,
           D/F#   **Gsus2**   **D/F#**   **Em7**
A no-smoking sign on your cigarette break.
            D/F#   **Gsus2**
It's like ten thousand spoons
               D/F#   **Em7**
When all you need is a knife,
         D/F#   **Gsus2**
It's meeting the man of my dreams
             D/F#   **Em7**
And then meeting his beautiful wife.
          D/F# **Gsus2**   **D/F#**   **Em7**
And isn't it ironic? don't you think?
          D/F# **Gsus2**   **D/F#**   **Em7**
A little too ironic, and yeah, I really do think.

Chorus 3   As Chorus 1

      Cmaj7 D6/4   **Cmaj7**   **D6/4**
Outro   And you know life has a funny way of sneaking up on you,
      Cmaj7   **D6/4**   **Cmaj7**
Life has a funny, funny way of helping you out.

Helping you out.

RIGHT THROUGH YOU

Music by Alanis Morissette and Glenn Ballard ▪ Lyrics by Alanis Morissette

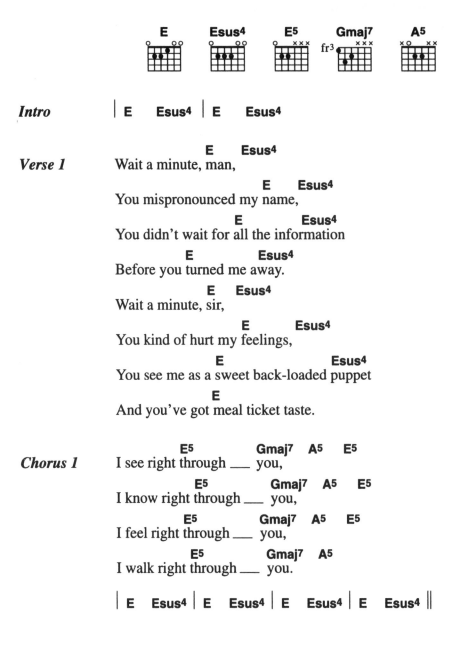

Intro | E   Esus⁴ | E   Esus⁴ |

Verse 1

     E Esus⁴
Wait a minute, man,

      E Esus⁴
You mispronounced my name,

       E Esus⁴
You didn't wait for all the information

     E Esus⁴
Before you turned me away.

     E Esus⁴
Wait a minute, sir,

       E Esus⁴
You kind of hurt my feelings,

      E   Esus⁴
You see me as a sweet back-loaded puppet

     E
And you've got meal ticket taste.

Chorus 1

    E⁵   Gmaj⁷ A⁵ E⁵
I see right through ___ you,

     E⁵   Gmaj⁷ A⁵ E⁵
I know right through ___ you,

    E⁵   Gmaj⁷ A⁵ E⁵
I feel right through ___ you,

    E⁵   Gmaj⁷ A⁵
I walk right through ___ you.

| E   Esus⁴ | E   Esus⁴ | E   Esus⁴ | E   Esus⁴ ‖

Verse 2

       E Esus⁴
You took me for a joke,

      E Esus⁴
You took me for a child,

     E   Esus⁴
You took a long hard look at my ass

       E   Esus⁴
And then played golf for a while.

       E Esus⁴
Your shake is like a fish,

      E Esus⁴
You pat me on the head,

     E   Esus⁴
You took me out to wine, dine, sixty-nine me,

       E
But didn't hear a damn word I said.

Chorus 2   As Chorus 1

Verse 3

      E Esus⁴
Well, hello Mister Man,

      E   Esus⁴
You didn't think I'd come back,

      E   Esus⁴
You didn't think I'd show up with my army

     E   Esus⁴
And this ammunition on my back.

     E   Esus⁴
Now that I'm Miss Thing,

     E   Esus⁴
Now that I'm a zillionaire,

    E   Esus⁴
You scan the credits for your name

     E
And wonder why it's not there.

Chorus 3

    E⁵   Gmaj⁷ A⁵ E⁵
I see right through __ you,

     E⁵   Gmaj⁷ A⁵ E⁵
I know right through __ you,

    E⁵   Gmaj⁷ A⁵ E⁵
I feel right through __ you,

    E⁵   Gmaj⁷ A⁵
I walk right through __ you.

GOODNIGHT GIRL

Words and Music by Graeme Clark, Tom Cunningham, Neil Mitchell & Marti Pellow

Verse 1

A
You hear me so clearly

Dmaj7
And see how I try.

A
You feel me, so heal me

Dmaj7
And tear me apart.

Gmaj7
And I won't tell a soul,

A
I won't tell at all.

Gmaj7
And do they have to know

Bm7
(Do they have to know)

Bm7/E   **A**
About my goodnight girl?

Chorus 1

(A)
Caught up in your wishing well,

F#m
Your hopes inside it,

Bm7
Take your love and promises and make them last,

Bm7/E
You make them last.

Verse 2

        A
You keep me so near you
        Dmaj7
And see me so far.
        A
And hold me and send me,
Dmaj7
Deep in your heart.
        Gmaj7
And I won't tell a soul,
        A
I won't tell at all.
        Gmaj7
And I won't let them know
             Bm7
(I won't let them know)
     Bm7/E   **A**
About my goodnight girl.

Chorus 2

        (A)
Caught up in your wishing well,
            F♯m
Your hopes inside it,
                       Bm7
Take your love and promises and make them last,
        Bm7/E
You make them last.

Chorus 3   As Chorus 2

Middle

Dmaj9   **Amaj7**   **Dmaj9**
  Doesn't matter how sad I made you,
                    Amaj7   **Dmaj9**
Doesn't matter how hard I've tried.
                    Amaj9
Just remember the same old reason
        Cmaj7
Reflected in your eyes, you said you wanted me.

Chorus 4   As Chorus 2

Chorus 5   As Chorus 2

LOVE IS ALL AROUND

Words and Music by Reg Presley

F **Bb/F** **F7** **Bb** **Cm** (fr3) **Eb** (fr6) **Fsus4**

Intro | F   Bb/F | F7   Bb/F | F   Bb/F | F7

Verse 1
```
       Bb          Cm    Eb      F       Bb  Cm | Eb  F
I feel it in my fingers, I feel it in my toes,
       Bb          Cm       Eb       F        Bb  Cm | Eb  F
The love that's all around me, and so the feeling grows,
       Bb          Cm  Eb       F        Bb  Cm | Eb  F
It's written on the wind, it's everywhere I go,
       Bb          Cm       Eb           F      Bb  Cm | Eb  F | F    || Eb
So if you really love me, come on and let it show.
```

Chorus 1
```
                         Cm         Eb
You know I love you, I always will,
                       Bb
My mind's made up by the way I feel.
         Eb                    Cm
There's no beginning, there'll be no end,
                    F          F7
'Cause on my love you can depend.
```

Instrumental | Bb   Cm | Eb   Fsus4 F | Bb   Cm | Eb   Fsus4 F

Verse 2
```
       Bb          Cm    Eb      F       Bb  Cm | Eb  F
I see your face before me as I lay on my bed,
       Bb          Cm     Eb       F         Bb  Cm | Eb  F
I cannot get to thinking of all the things you said.
        Bb                Cm   Eb       F        Bb  Cm | Eb  F
You gave your promise to me and I gave mine to you,
        Bb          Cm     Eb       F      Bb  Cm | Eb  F | F    || Eb
I need someone beside me in everything I do.
```

Chorus 2

  (E♭)   **Cm** **E♭**
You know I love you, I always will,

          B♭
My mind's made up by the way I feel.

   E♭   **Cm**
There's no beginning, there'll be no end,

       F   **F7** **B♭/F** | **F7** **B♭/F** | **F**
'Cause on my love you can depend.

    B♭/F **F7**
Got to keep it moving.

Verse 3

    B♭   **Cm** **E♭** **Fsus4** **F** **B♭** **Cm** | **E♭** **F**
It's written in the wind, oh, everywhere I go,

   B♭   **Cm** **E♭** **Fsus4** **F** **B♭** **Cm** | **E♭**
So if you really love me, come on and let it show,

  F
Come on and let it (show).

  B♭   **Cm**
‖: Come on and let it,

E♭   **Fsus4** **F**
Come on and let it,

B♭   **Cm** **E♭** **Fsus4** **F**
Come on and let it show.   :‖ *Repeat to fade*

SWEET SURRENDER

Words and Music by Graeme Clark, Tom Cunningham, Neil Mitchell & Marti Pellow

G   Em7   Am7   B7   C   Am7♭5   fr4   D/G   Bm7   Am/G

Intro   ‖: G | Em7 | Am7 | Am7 :‖

Verse 1
G   Em7
Hey little fella, get your show together,
Am7   G
I was listening before, now I don't care no more.
                        Em7
Look around now, look around now,
                    Am7
It's always that it's gonna get me down,
                        G
It's only begun, yeah.

Chorus 1
                    B7
One look is all it took,
C   Am7♭5   G
Ooh, I remember that sweet surrender,
      Em7   Am7   G   D/G
I recall, do you, that sweet surrender,
          Am7 | Am7 ‖ G
Sweet surrender.

Verse 2
              Em7   Am7
My determination
                                    G
Came creeping across the nation,
                  Em7
A sure mistake for anyone,
                      Am7
So you can't take home everyone,
                      G
'Cause it's only just begun.

Chorus 2

  (G)   **B7**   **C**
One look was all it took
          Am7♭5   **G**
To remember that sweet surrender,
     Em7   **Am7**   **G**
I recall, do you, that sweet surrender.

Bridge 1

        Em7   **Bm7**
I don't know, I don't care,

'Cause I'm living without you baby,
B7   **C** **Am7♭5**
Even when I know what's going on, yeah, it only took
G   **B7**
One look, one glance,
C   **Am7♭5**   **G**
Ooh, and it set my heart, set for romance.
        Em7   **Am7**   **G**   **D/G**
Do you believe my sweet surrender,
            Am/G
My sweet surrender?

Verse 3

  G   **Em7**
Hey little fella, now your show's together,
      Am7
I never wanted you to listen before,
                  G
So why should I walk out the door.
         Em7
Stick around now,
        Am7
And so the story goes on through the night,
      G
It's only begun.

Chorus 3

     B7   **C**
One look is all it took,
     Am7♭5   **G**
I remember that sweet surrender,
     Em7   **Am7**   **G**
Do you recall, 'cause I do, my sweet surrender.

Continued on next page...

Bridge 2

      Em7   Bm7
I don't know, I don't care,

'Cause I'm living without you baby,

B7   C Am7♭5
Even when I know what's going on, yeah, it's all it takes

G   B7
One look, one glance.

C   Am7♭5   G
Ooh, and it set my heart, set for romance.

    Em7 Am7   G
One look is all it took, my sweet surrender,

D/G   Am/G G
My sweet surrender.

   (G)   D/G   Am/G G
‖: One look is all it took remember. :‖ *Repeat ad lib. to fade*

ODE TO MY FAMILY

Words and Music by Dolores O'Riordan & Noel Hogan

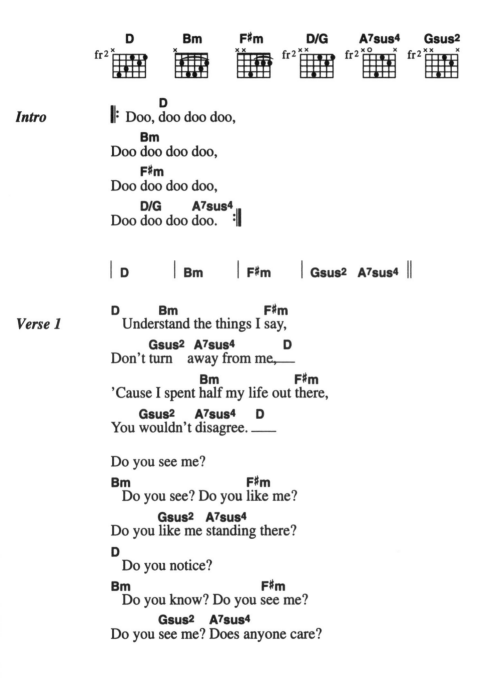

Intro

‖: Doo, doo doo doo,
(D)

Doo doo doo doo,
(Bm)

Doo doo doo doo,
(F#m)

Doo doo doo doo. :‖
(D/G) (A7sus4)

| D | Bm | F#m | Gsus2 A7sus4 ‖

Verse 1

    D   Bm   F#m
Understand the things I say,

    Gsus2 A7sus4   D
Don't turn   away from me,___

           Bm   F#m
'Cause I spent half my life out there,

    Gsus2 A7sus4 D
You wouldn't disagree. ___

Do you see me?

Bm   **F#m**
  Do you see? Do you like me?

     Gsus2 A7sus4
Do you like me standing there?

D
  Do you notice?

Bm   **F#m**
  Do you know? Do you see me?

    Gsus2 A7sus4
Do you see me? Does anyone care?

Chorus 1

    D   Bm   F#m
Unhappiness where's when I was young

        Gsus2   A7sus4   D
And we didn't give a damn, ___

                Bm
'Cause we were raised

        F#m   Gsus2 A7sus4   D
To see life as fun and take it if we can. ___

                Bm   F#m
My mother, my mother she hold me,

        Gsus2   A7sus4
She hold me when I was out there.

D   Bm   F#m
  My father, my father he liked me,

        Gsus2   A7sus4
Oh, he liked me. Does anyone care?

    | D | Bm | F#m | Gsus2 A7sus4 ‖

Verse 2

D   Bm   F#m
  Understand what I've become,

Gsus2 A7sus4   D
It wasn't my design, ___

           Bm
And people ev'rywhere think

F#m   Gsus2 A7sus4   D
Something better   than I am. ___

           Bm
I miss you,

          F#m
I miss, 'cause I liked it,

         Gsus2 A7sus4
'Cause I liked it when I was out there.

D   Bm
  Do you know this?

                  F#m
Do you know you did not find me?

        Gsus2 A7sus4
You did not find, does anyone care?

Chorus 2

$\quad$ D $\qquad$ Bm $\qquad\qquad$ F#m
$\quad$ Unhappiness where's when I was young

$\qquad\qquad$ Gsus2 $\qquad$ A7sus4 $\quad$ D
And we didn't give a $\quad$ damn, ____

$\qquad\qquad\qquad$ Bm
'Cause we were raised

$\qquad$ F#m $\qquad\qquad$ Gsus2 A7sus4 $\qquad$ D
To see life as fun and take $\;$ it $\;$ if we can. ____

$\qquad\qquad$ Bm $\qquad\qquad$ F#m
My mother, $\;$ my mother she hold me,

$\qquad$ Gsus2 $\qquad\qquad$ A7sus4
She hold me when I was out there.

D $\qquad\qquad$ Bm $\qquad\qquad$ F#m
$\quad$ My father, $\;$ my father he liked me.

$\qquad$ Gsus2
Oh, he liked me.

$\qquad$ A7sus4 $\qquad\qquad$ D
Does anyone care? ____

$\qquad\qquad\qquad$ Bm
Does anyone care? ____

$\qquad\qquad\qquad$ F#m
Does anyone care? ____

$\qquad\qquad\qquad$ Gsus2
Does anyone care? ____

$\qquad$ A7sus4 $\qquad\qquad$ D
Does anyone care? ____

$\qquad\qquad\qquad$ Bm
Does anyone care? ____

$\qquad\qquad\qquad$ F#m
Does anyone care? ____

$\qquad\qquad\qquad$ Gsus2 $\quad$ A7sus4
Does anyone care? ____

Outro

$\qquad\qquad$ D
||: Doo, doo doo doo,

$\qquad$ Bm
Doo doo doo doo,

$\qquad$ F#m
Doo doo doo doo,

$\qquad$ D/G $\qquad$ A7sus4
Doo doo doo doo $\quad$:|| $\;$ *Play 3 times*

| D $\quad$ | Bm $\quad$ | F#m $\quad$ | D $\quad$ ||

NOT SORRY

Words by Dolores O'Riordan ▪ Music by Noel Hogan & Dolores O'Riordan

Am2   C/F   C   G6   G6/D   Fmaj7   Am

Intro

‖: | Am2 | C/F | C | G6 |

| Am2 | C/F | C | G6 :‖

Verse 1

Am2   C/F
Keep on looking through the window again,
   C   G6/D
But I'm not sorry if I do insult you,
    Am2   C/F
I'm sad, not sorry, 'bout the way that things went,
    C   G6
And you'll be happy and I'll be forsakin' thee.

Verse 2

   Am2   C/F
I swore I'd never feel like this again,
    C   G6/D
But you're so selfish you don't see what you're doing to me,
   Am2   C/F
I keep on looking through the window again.
    C   G6   Am2
No, I'm not sorry If I do insult you, ____
   C/F   G6   Fmaj7
No, I'm not sorry if I do insult you. ____

Chorus 1

              Am
You told me lies and I sighed, and I sighed,

                    Fmaj7
And I sighed, 'cause you lied,

          Am
Lied, and I cried, yes I cried,

                  Fmaj7
Yes I cry, I cry, I try again.

        Am
I realise, as he sighed, and he sighed,

               Fmaj7
And he sighed 'cause you lied,

            Am
Lied and I cried, yes I cried,

Yes I cry, I cry, I try again.

Verse 3   As Verse 1

Verse 4

Am2   **C/F**
I swore I'd never feel like this again,

   C   **G6/D**
But you're so selfish you don't see what you're doing to me,

Am2   **C/F**
I keep on looking through the window again.

   C   **G6**   **Am2**
No, I'm not sorry if I do detest you, ___

   C/F   **G6**   **Fmaj7**
No, I'm not sorry if I do detest you. ___

Chorus 2   As Chorus 1

Outro

Am2   **C/F**   **C**   **G6/D**
Keep on looking through the window again,

Am2   **C/F**   **C**   **G6**
Keep on looking through the window again.

‖: **Am2** | **C/F** | **C** | **G6**   :‖ **Am2**   ‖

EVERYTHING I SAID

Words by Dolores O'Riordan ▪ Music by Dolores O'Riordan & Noel Hogan

Cmaj7   C   Em   C2/E   Fmaj9#11   Fmaj9

G6   G5/6   Fmaj7   Am   Em/B   G6*

Capo 3rd fret

Intro

| Cmaj7 | C   Cmaj7 | Em | C2/E | |

| Fmaj9#11   Fmaj9 | G6 | G5/6   G6 |

Verse 1

Cmaj7   C   Cmaj7
  It makes me lonely, ____

  Em   C2/E
It makes me very lonely

    Fmaj9#11   Fmaj9   G6   G5/6   G6
When I see you here,   waitin' on.

Cmaj7   C   Cmaj7
  It makes me tired, ____

  Em   C2/E
It makes me very tired,

    Fmaj9#11   Fmaj9   G6   G5/6   G6
And inside of me,   lingers on.

Verse 2

    Cmaj7   C   Cmaj7
But you have your heart, oh,

  Em   C2/E
Don't believe it, ____

    Fmaj9#11   Fmaj9   G6   G5/6   G6
And you ran outside,   waiting on. ____

    Cmaj7   C   Cmaj7
Ev'rything I said, oh,

  Em   C2/E
Well I meant it, ____

    Fmaj9#11   Fmaj9   G6   G5/6   G6
And inside my head,   holdin' on.

Bridge

Fmaj7   Am
 'Cause if I died tonight,

              Em/B
Would you hold my head, oh,

             G6*
Would you understand? ____

Fmaj7   Am
  And if I lied in spite,

             Em/B
Would you still be here, no,

          G6*
Would you disappear?

Verse 3

Cmaj7 C   Cmaj7 Em
    Surely must be you,

C2/E   Fmaj9#11
Surely must be you,

     Fmaj9   G6   G5/6 G6
But I don't make you lonely,   la.

Cmaj7 C   Cmaj7 Em
   I'll get over   you,

C2/E   Fmaj9#11
I'll get over you,

     Fmaj9   G6   G5/6 G6
But I don't make you lonely,   la.

Outro

‖: Cmaj7   Em
  La, da, da, da, da, da.

C2/E   Fmaj9#11
La, da, da, da, da,

Fmaj9   G6   G5/6 G6
La, da, da, da, da, da, da,   la. :‖

Cmaj7
  La, da, da, da, da, da,

La, da, da, da, da, da.

15 YEARS

Words & Music by Simon Friend, Charles Heather, Mark Chadwick, Jonathon Sevink & Jeremy Cunningham

Am   G   Dm   F   Em

Intro   ‖: Am | Am | G | Am :‖

Verse 1
Am
"I never was a violent man,"
　　　　　G　　　　　　　　　Am
Said the man in the bar with his head in his hands.

He's trying his best to understand
　　G　　　　　　　Am
The cause of his dismay.

But the years of gin have broken him,
　　　　　G　　　　　　　　Am
They've left him cold where he fitted in.

But it's too late now to turn around
　　　　G　　　　　Am
And find another way.

Chorus 1
　　　　　　　Dm　　　　　　　　　F
And the laughs in the late night lock-in
Am　　　　　　　　　G
Are fading away when he gets in,
　　Dm　　　　　　F
The girl from fifteen years ago
Am
Has packed and gone away.

Instrumental   ‖: Am | Am | G | Am :‖

Verse 2
               Am
"That's never how it used to be,

        G   **Am**
What happened to all that energy?

You took one too many liberties,

        G   **Am**
I'm tired of being afraid."

So the night after the fight she took flight,

        G   **Am**
Hiding swollen eyes and a wounded pride,

The best years of her life denied

        G   **Am**
And sold for liquid shares.

Chorus 2   As Chorus 1

        (Am)   **Em**   **C**   **G**
Middle   And the victims of their world are advertised on posters,

            Am   **Em** **C**   **G**
Just a beach and a pretty girl   if you take this potion.

            Am
Verse 3   It's another week till his cheque comes through,

        G   **Am**
He's got a fiver left now to spend on food,

But the doors of the bar are open,

        G   **Am**
And he breaks another rule.

Well he sits on a stool that bears his name,

        G   **Am**
He's got a favourite glass that's called the same,

He's never been kept waiting

        G   **Am**
'Cos he pays the landlord's wage.

Chorus 3   As Chorus 1

Chorus 4   As Chorus 1

C.C.T.V.

Words & Music by Simon Friend, Charles Heather, Mark Chadwick, Jonathon Sevink & Jeremy Cunningham

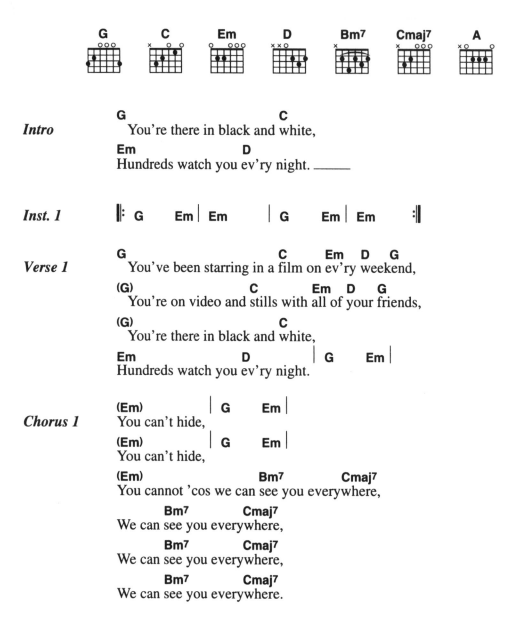

Intro

G   C
You're there in black and white,
Em   D
Hundreds watch you ev'ry night. _____

Inst. 1

‖: G   Em | Em | G   Em | Em   :‖

Verse 1

G   C   Em D G
You've been starring in a film on ev'ry weekend,
(G)   C   Em D G
You're on video and stills with all of your friends,
(G)   C
You're there in black and white,
Em   D | G   Em |
Hundreds watch you ev'ry night.

Chorus 1

(Em) | G   Em |
You can't hide,
(Em) | G   Em |
You can't hide,
(Em)   Bm⁷   Cmaj⁷
You cannot 'cos we can see you everywhere,
    Bm⁷   Cmaj⁷
We can see you everywhere,
    Bm⁷   Cmaj⁷
We can see you everywhere,
    Bm⁷   Cmaj⁷
We can see you everywhere.

Verse 2

   G   C   Em D   G
You're great in every scene, you're very natural,

  (G)   C   Em   D G
It's as if you cannot see the spotlight on you,

  (G)   C
But when you fluff a line

       Em   D | G   Em |
The director says you're doing time.

Chorus 2   As Chorus 1

Middle

  G   A
When you're walking home

     D   G
In the evenin' after dark,

  Em   G   Em   G
Remember don't hide and show your best side

       D   C
'Cos you're a star in a film.

Inst. 2 ‖: G   Em | Em | G   Em | Em   :‖ G   Em |

  (Em) | G   Em |
You can't hide.

  (Em) | G   Em ‖
You can't hide.

Chorus 3   As Chorus 1

    | G   Em | Em   ‖

BELARUSE

Words & Music by Simon Friend, Charles Heather, Mark Chadwick, Jonathon Sevink & Jeremy Cunningham

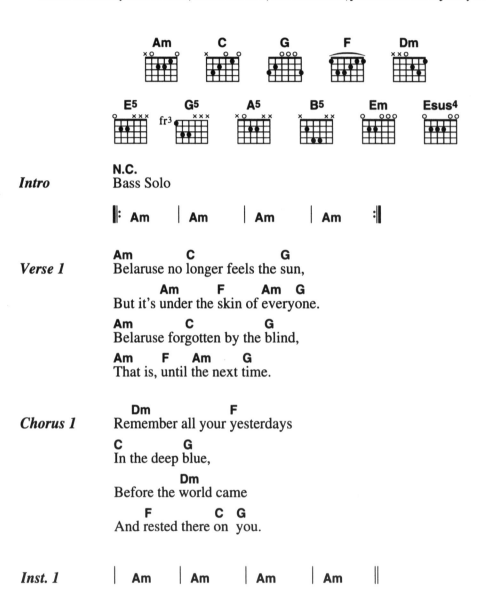

Intro

N.C.
Bass Solo

‖: Am | Am | Am | Am :‖

Verse 1

Am   C   G
Belaruse no longer feels the sun,

         Am   F   Am G
But it's under the skin of everyone.

Am   C   G
Belaruse forgotten by the blind,

Am   F   Am   G
That is, until the next time.

Chorus 1

       Dm   F
Remember all your yesterdays

C   G
In the deep blue,

         Dm
Before the world came

     F   C G
And rested there on you.

Inst. 1

| Am | Am | Am | Am ‖

Verse 1

    Am   **C**   **G**
And if the sun and moon were both to doubt,

Am **F**   **Am** **G**
Sure enough they'd both go out.

             Am   **C**   **G**
When you can't walk in your field, feel water in your hands,

Am   **F**   **Am** **G**
You've been touched by the doubt of man.

Chorus 2

   Dm   **F**
Remember all your yesterdays

C   **G**
In the deep blue,

      Dm
Before the world came

   F   **C G**
And rested there on you.

Inst. 2

‖: E5 G5 E5 G5 | E5 A5 E5 A5 |

| E5 B5 E5 B5 | B5 A5 G5   :‖   *Play 3 times*

‖: Em   Esus4 | Em   Esus4 :‖

| E5 G5 E5 G5 | E5 A5 E5 A5 | E5 B5 E5 B5 | B5 A5 G5   ‖

Chorus 3

   Dm   **F**
Remember all your yesterdays

C   **G**
In the deep blue,

      Dm
Before the world came

   F   **C G**
And rested there on you.

Outro

N.C.
Bass Solo

‖: E5 G5 E5 G5 | E5 A5 E5 A5 |

| E5 B5 E5 B5 | B5 A5 G5   :‖   *Play 4 times*

| E5   ‖

MADE OF STONE

Words & Music by Ian Brown & John Squire

Em7 **Em6** **Cmaj7/E** ***Em** **Em** **D** **C** **B** **G**

Intro   ‖: Em7 | Em6 | Cmaj7/E | *Em :‖

Verse 1

Em   D
Your knuckles whiten on the wheel,

                          C
The last thing that your hands will feel,

                    B
Your final flight can't be delayed.

Em   D
No earth, just sky it's so serene,

                    C
Your pink fat lips let go a scream,

                  B
You fry and melt, I love the scene.

Chorus 1

               G   D   C
Sometimes I fantasize when the streets are cold and lonely

            G
And the cars they burn below me.

                      D   C
Don't these times fill your eyes when the streets are cold and lonely

            G
And the cars they burn below me,

              D   Em
Are you alone, is anybody home?

Link | Em | Em | D | D |
| C | C | B | B ‖

Verse 2

```
Em                          D
I'm standing warm against the cold,
                            C
Now that the flames have taken hold
                          B
At least you left your life in style.
Em                    D
And for as far as I can see,
                        C
Ten twisted grilles grin back at me,
                      B
Bad money dies, I love the scene.
```

Chorus 2   As Chorus 1

Solo

| Em | Em | D | D | |
| C | C | B | B | :‖ *Play 3 times*

Chorus 3

```
          G     D            C
Sometimes I fantasize when the streets are cold and lonely
          G
And the cars they burn below me.
                      D            C
Don't these times fill your eyes when the streets are cold and lonely.
              G
And the cars they burn below me,
              D                    Em
Are you alone, are you made of stone?
```

Outro

‖: Em⁷ | Em⁶ | Cmaj⁷/E | *Em :‖

SHE BANGS THE DRUMS

Words & Music by Ian Brown & John Squire

E   **Esus4**   **D**   **A**   **Asus4**

Intro   ‖: **E** | **E**   **Esus4** :‖

Verse 1

      E   **Esus4** **E**
I can feel the earth begin to move,

                Esus4 D
I hear my needle hit the groove.

And spiral through another day,

                  E
I hear my song begin to say:

             Esus4   **E**
"Kiss me where the sun don't shine,

                   Esus4 D
The past was yours but the future's mine,

You're all out of time."

Verse 2

      E   **Esus4** **E**
I don't feel too steady on my feet,

             Esus4 D
I feel hollow, I feel   weak.

Passion fruit and Holy bread

               E
Fill my guts and ease my head.

             Esus4   **E**
Through the early morning sun

         Esus4   **D**
I can see her, here she comes,

She bangs the drums.

Chorus 1

A   D   A
Have you seen her, have you heard?
            D   A
The way she plays, there are no words
       D   E
To describe the way I feel.
A   D   A
How could it ever come to pass?
         D   A
She'll be the first, she'll be the last
       D   E
To describe the way I feel, the way I feel.

Instrumental

‖: Asus⁴ | A | Esus⁴ | E   :‖

| E | E | E | E | D | D | D | D |

| E | E | E | E | D | D | D | D E ‖

Chorus 2   As Chorus 1

Chorus 3   As Chorus 1

Outro   *Instrumental as Chorus to fade*

WHAT THE WORLD IS WAITING FOR

Words & Music by Ian Brown & John Squire

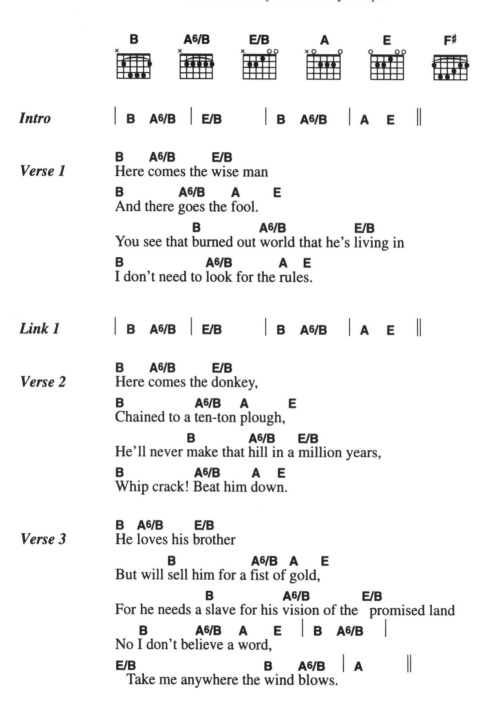

Intro

|| B A6/B | E/B | B A6/B | A E ||

Verse 1

B   A6/B   E/B
Here comes the wise man

B   A6/B   A   E
And there goes the fool.

          B   A6/B   E/B
You see that burned out world that he's living in

B   A6/B   A E
I don't need to look for the rules.

Link 1

|| B A6/B | E/B | B A6/B | A E ||

Verse 2

B   A6/B   E/B
Here comes the donkey,

B   A6/B A   E
Chained to a ten-ton plough,

          B   A6/B E/B
He'll never make that hill in a million years,

B   A6/B   A E
Whip crack! Beat him down.

Verse 3

B A6/B   E/B
He loves his brother

           B   A6/B A   E
But will sell him for a fist of gold,

             B   A6/B   E/B
For he needs a slave for his vision of the   promised land

    B   A6/B   A   E | B A6/B |
No I don't believe a word,

E/B   B   A6/B | A ||
   Take me anywhere the wind blows.

	F# E
Chorus 1	You'll never know just what you wanna do
	A
	Or where you want to go.
	E
	I think it's time
	B A
	That you found what the world is waiting for,
	F# B
	I think it's time _____ to get real.

Link 2 |: B A6/B | E/B | B A6/B | A   E :||

Verse 4 As Verse 1

Verse 5 As Verse 3

Chorus 2 As Chorus 1

Link 3 |: B A6/B | E/B | B A6/B | A   E :||

	F# B
Bridge	Anytime you want it then it's there
	E B
	All you've got to do is stop me on a corner and ask,
	F# B
	Say, hey! You don't live today,
	E F#
	Stop the world, stop the world,
	B A6/B	E/B	B A6/B	
	I'm getting off, I'm getting off,
	A E B A6/B	E/B	B A6/B	A E :||
	Can't get enough, I'm getting off.

Outro |: B A6/B | E/B | B A6/B | A   E :|| *Ad lib. to fade*

BULL-RUSH

Words & Music by Paul Weller

Chord diagrams: E   D   C#m (fr4)   Bm7   Dsus2   Em7   A

Esus4   Asus4   G5   Am/D   Gm7/C   Fm7/B♭ (fr5)   Dm7/11 (fr7)   A11

Intro ‖ E | D | C#m | Bm7 | E | D | E | D ‖

Verse 1

    E   D   Dsus2
In a momentary lapse of my condition,

    E   D   Dsus2
Sent me tumbling down into a deep despair,

    E   D   Dsus2
Lost and dazed so I had no real recollection,

Em7   A   E   Esus4
Until the rain cleared the air.

Verse 2

    E   D   Dsus2
When you wake to find that everything has left you,

    E   D   Dsus2
And the clothes you wear belong to someone else,

    E   D   Dsus2
See your shadow chasing off towards the shore line,

Em7   A   E
Drifting into emptiness.

Chorus 1

            D   Dsus2 E   Esus4 E
There are bull rushes outside my window,

          Asus4   A   E   Esus4 E
And their leaves whisper words in the breeze,

      D   Dsus2 E
Well tomorrow I'll walk to the harbour,

      G5   A   E Esus4
Catch the first boat that's coming in,

  E   G5   A   E   Esus4 E
I'll catch the first boat that's coming in.

Verse 3

   (E)   **D**   **Dsus^2**
Like a child too small to reach the front door handle,

   E   **D**   **Dsus^2**
Or maybe just too scared to know what I would find,

   E   **D**   **Dsus^2**
Now I feel I'm strong enough to take the slow ride

   Em^7   **A**   **E** **Esus^4** **E**
Not knowing when I will arrive.

Chorus 2   As Chorus 1

Middle

   D   **E**
I do believe I'm going home,

   D   **E**
'Cause I don't call this place my own,

   Bm^7   **A**
I'm missing what I had,

   Am/D   **Gm^7/C**
Happy times and sad,

          Fm^7/B$\flat$
More than I ever thought could be.

Instrumental | **Dm^7/11** | **A^{11}** | **Dm^7/11** | **A^{11}** ||

   E   **D**
La la la la la la la la la la la la,

   E   **D**
La la la la la la la la la la la,

   E   **D**
La la la la la la la la la la la,

   Em^7   **A**   **E**
Not knowing when I will arrive.

Chorus 3   As Chorus 1

Outro

   E   **G^5**   **A**   **E** **Esus^4**
I'll catch the first boat that's coming in, yeah,

   G^5 A   **G^5 A**   **G^5 A**   **E**
   Yeah,   yeah,   that's coming in.

Instrumental ‖: **E** | **D** **Dsus^2** | **E** | **D** **Dsus^2** :‖ *Play 4 times*

                 ‖: **E** **D E** | **E** **D E** | **E** **D E** | **E** **D E** :‖ *Repeat to fade*

YOU DO SOMETHING TO ME

Words & Music by Paul Weller

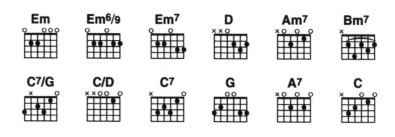

Intro | Em Em6/9 Em7 | Em Em6/9 Em7 | Em Em6/9 Em7 | Em   ‖

Verse 1

(Em)   D   Am7
You do something to me,

Bm7   Em
Something deep inside.

             D   Am7
I'm hanging on the wire

       Bm7   Em
For the love I'll never find.

Verse 2

              D   Am7
You do something wonderful

   Bm7   Em
Then chase it all away.

         D   Am7
Mixing my emotions,

    Bm7   Em
That throws me back again.

Chorus 1

         C7/G   Am7
Hanging on the wire, yeah,

  C/D   Em
I'm waiting for the change.

C7   G
  I'm dancing through the fire

   A7   C   C/D Em
Just to catch a flame and feel real again.

Guitar solo   ‖: D | Am⁷   Bm⁷ | Em | Em   :‖

Chorus 2   As Chorus 1

                (Em)   D   Am⁷
Verse 3   You do something to me,
                Bm⁷   Em
                Somewhere deep inside.
                                 D   Am⁷
                I'm hoping to get close to
                   Bm⁷   Em
                A peace I cannot find.

                                 C⁷/G   Am⁷
Chorus 3   Dancing through the fire, yeah,
                C/D   Em
                Just to catch a flame.
                C⁷   G
                   Just to get close to,
                     A⁷   C⁷   C/D Em
                Just close enough to tell you that:
                                 D   Am⁷
                You do something to me,
                Bm⁷   Em   Em⁶/⁹ Em⁷
                   Something deep inside.

                | Em Em⁶/⁹ Em⁷ | Em Em⁶/⁹ Em⁷ | Em Em⁶/⁹ Em⁷ | Em   ‖

BAR ITALIA

Music by Pulp ▪ Lyrics by Jarvis Cocker

C   E   Am   F   Fm   B♭

Intro | C | C   ‖

Verse 1

   C   E
  Now if you can stand,
      Am   F
I would like to take you by the hand, yeah,
 C   E
  And go for a walk,
    Am   F
Past people as they go to work.
 C   E
  Let's get out of this place before
    Am   Fm
They tell us that we've just died, oh.

Chorus 1

 C   E
Move, move quick, you've gotta move,
    Am   Fm
Come on it's through, come on it's time,
       C   E
Oh, look at you, you're looking so confused,
     Am Fm
Just what did you lose, oh.

    | C | C   ‖

Verse 2

C   E
If you can make

  Am   F
An order, could you get me one?

C   E
Two sugars would be great

  Am   F
'Cos I'm fading fast and it's nearly dawn.

C   E
If they knocked down this place, this place,

  Am   Fm
It'd still look much better than you, oh now.

Chorus 2   As Chorus 1

C
It's O.K. it's just your mind.

Instrumental ‖: C | E | Am | Fm   :‖

C   E
If we get through this ali-hi-hive,

        Am   Fm
I'll meet you next week, same place, same time, oh.

Chorus 3   As Chorus 1

Outro

C
That's what you get from clubbing it,

    E
You can't go home and go to bed

  Am
Because it hasn't worn off yet,

  Fm
And now it's morning.

    C
There's only one place we can go,

    E
It's around the corner in Soho

   Am   Fm
Where other broken people go.

B♭ C
Let's go.

MIS-SHAPES

Music by Pulp ▪ Lyrics by Jarvis Cocker

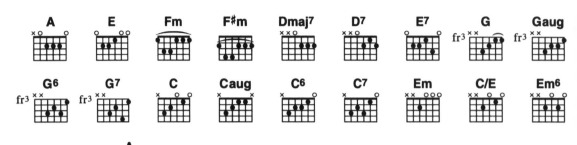

Verse 1

A
Mis-shapes, mistakes, misfits,

E   **Fm**
Raised on a diet of broken biscuits, oh,

F#m
 We don't look the same as you,

Dmaj7
 And we don't do the things you do,

  D7
But we live 'round here too, oh really.

Verse 2

A
Mis-shapes, mistakes, misfits,

   E   **Fm**
We'd like to go to town but we can't risk it, oh,

F#m
 'Cause they just want to keep us out,

Dmaj7
 You could end up with a smack in the mouth

D7
Just for standing out, now really.

A   **E7**
 Brother, sisters, can't you see

      E   **Fm F#m**
The future's owned by you and me?

         Dmaj7
There won't be fighting in the street,

They think they've got us beat,

   D7   **G**
But revenge is going to be so sweet, oh. ____

      (G)   Gaug   G6
We're making a move, we're making it now,

                G7
We're coming out of the sidelines.

  C   Caug   C6
  Just put your hands up, it's a raid, yeah.

C7   Em   C/E
  We want your homes, we want your lives,

           Em6   C/E
We want the things you won't allow us,

           Em   C/E
We won't use guns, we won't use bombs,

           Em6   C/E
We'll use the one thing we've got more of,

         Em
That's our minds.

Verse 3

    A
Check your lucky numbers,

    E   Fm
That much money could drag you under, oh,

F#m
  What's the point of being rich

Dmaj7
If you can't think what to do with it,

       D7
'Cause you're so bleeding thick.

    A   E7
  Oh, we weren't supposed to be,

         E
We learnt too much at school,

Fm   F#m
Now we can't help but see

     Dmaj7
The future that you've got mapped out

    D7   G
Is nothing much to shout about, oh. ____

Chorus 2   As Chorus 1

Instrumental | E | E ||

                | A | A | E | E   Fm | F#m |

                | F#m | Dmaj7 | Dmaj7 | D7 | D7 ||

Verse 4

        A   **E⁷**
And brother, sisters, can't you see

         E   **Fm F♯m**
The future's owned by you and me?

                         Dmaj⁷
There won't be fighting in the street,

They think that they've got us beat,

     D⁷   **G**
But revenge is going to be so sweet.

Chorus 2

                Gaug   **G⁶**
We're making a move, we're making it now,

               G⁷
We're coming out of the sidelines.

C   **Caug**   **C⁶**
  Just put your hands up, it's a raid, yeah.

C⁷   **Em**   **C/E**
  We want your homes, we want your lives,

        Em⁶   **C/E**
We want the things you won't allow us,

        Em   **C/E**
We won't use guns, we won't use bombs,

        Em⁶   **C/E**
We'll use the one thing we've got more of,

       Em   **C/E**   **Em⁶** **C/E**
That's our minds, _____ yeah.

         Em   **C/E**   **Em⁶** **C/E** **A**
And that's our minds, _____ yeah.